Brain
BENDERS

RIDICULOUS
RIDDLES

ARCTURUS

ARCTURUS

This edition published in 2018 by Arcturus Publishing Limited
26/27 Bickels Yard, 151–153 Bermondsey Street,
London SE1 3HA

ISBN: 978-1-78828-067-9
CH005924NT
Supplier 10, Date 0918, Print run 7411

Written by Lisa Regan
Illustrations by Moreno Chiacchiera
Design by Notion Design

Printed in the UK

CONTENTS

Introduction

On the following pages, you'll find baffling brain-teasers, cunning conundrums, and ridiculous riddles that will give your mental muscles a real workout! The solutions can be straightforward, or they might require some head-scratching. Some will make you laugh, while others are sure to make you groan. Remember, all the answers are in the back, but try not to peek! Now it's time to get riddling!

Animal Riddles

1. What single letter can you swap to make a cold bear become hot?

2. What gets naked to keep you warm?

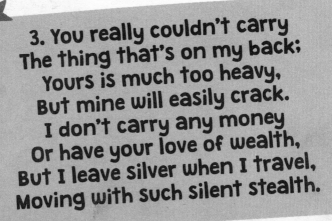

3. You really couldn't carry
The thing that's on my back;
Yours is much too heavy,
But mine will easily crack.
I don't carry any money
Or have your love of wealth,
But I leave silver when I travel,
Moving with such silent stealth.

Answers on page 102

4. A polar bear walks 3 miles north and then 2 miles south. He ends up 5 miles from his starting point. How can that be?

5. What kind of socks do polar bears wear?

6. Why do seagulls live by the sea?

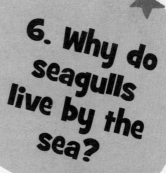

Answers on page 102

7. What do giraffes have that no other animal has, that keeps them from going extinct?

8. What type of animal works for the CIA?

8

9. I hiss like a frying pan and am made with an egg. I can move around, though I have no legs. My skin peels off, but I stay the same. I'm long and strong ... do you know my name?

10. The more you take, the more you leave behind. What are they?

11. Why don't lions eat stand-up comedians?

12. There are **25 mice** in a school classroom during a class. The mice are moving around, but nobody is looking at them. Why is that?

13. What kind of pet always lives on the floor?

14. What did the dentist say to the mouse when it broke a tooth?

Answers on page 103

15. Why are leopards no good at hiding?

16. Mystery Word

Each line of this puzzle is a clue to a letter. Can you discover the hidden word?

My first is in wild, and bellow, and water.
My second's in woman and also in daughter.
My third is the very beginning of rough.
My fourth is in bristles, in tusks, and in tough.
My fifth is in hairy and cough but not snout.
You're well on your way to working this out!
My sixth appears twice in the roots that I munch.
My last is in pig, who's one of my bunch.
What am I?

Answers on page 103

17. A frog sits on a lily pad in the middle of a circular pond. He is 40 feet from the edge. His first jump takes him to a lily pad 20 feet away. After his first jump, he always jumps half the distance of his previous jump. How many jumps must he make to reach dry land?

18. I have a bushy tail but do not sweep.
I stay awake while you're asleep.
Just like a wolf, my fur is brown.
I'm totally wild but live in town.
What am I?

19. How do you describe an exhausted frog?

12

Answers on page 103

20. Joe is taking his dog for a walk. It doesn't walk in front of him, or behind him, or to one side of him. He isn't carrying it, and of course, it isn't above him or below him. Where is his dog?

21. What do you call a lionfish with no eyes?

22. This case has no hinges, no key, no lid, but golden treasure inside is hid.

23. A cowboy rides into town on Friday, stays for two days, and leaves on Friday. How can that be?

24. I am a seven-letter word, but if you take away four letters, only one is left. I'm a real beast ... you might even say I'm the queen! Who am I?

25. What does a buffalo say to her son when he leaves for school?

Answers on page 104

26. A man must cross a river in his boat, taking with him a snake, his pet rat, and a sack of grain.

The boat is only big enough to carry the man and one item at a time.

He can't leave the snake and the rat together, and he can't leave the rat and the grain together.

How does he get everything safely across the river?

27. How do you get down from a donkey?

28. What animal can jump higher than an elephant?

29. What animal wears more in the summer than it does in the winter?

Answers on page 105

30. A monkey is tied to the end of a piece of string 3 feet long. How did it manage to eat some figs from a bowl 9 feet away?

31. What creature walks on four legs in the morning, two legs at noon, and three legs in the evening?

32. When is a rook not a bird?

33. When is a swan the same as corn?

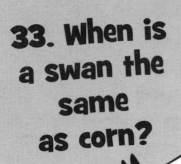

34. What has two heads and one tail, and walks on four legs?

35. I live in the river but don't have any fins. If you canoe past, I might tip you in. When it looks like I'm bored, I'm actually cross. Even the crocodiles know I'm the boss!

Answers on page 106

36. If two birds lay an average of three eggs every day, how many eggs can a peacock lay in three days?

37. What grows even though it is not alive?

38. What can you find in the middle of Uruguay that can't be found anywhere in Brazil or Bolivia?

Answers on page 106

39. This is a very old, traditional riddle:

As I was going to St. Ives, I met a man with seven wives. Each wife had seven sacks, and every sack had seven cats. Every cat had seven kittens. Kittens, cats, wives, sacks: How many were going to St. Ives?

40. If the alphabet goes from A to Z, what goes from Z to A?

Answers on page 106

Around the Home

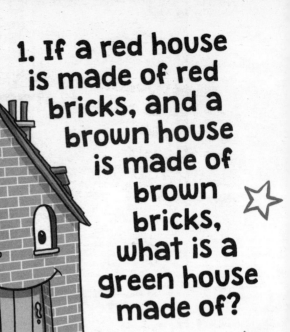

1. If a red house is made of red bricks, and a brown house is made of brown bricks, what is a green house made of?

2. What goes up and down the stairs without moving?

3. I turn around once;
What is out will not get in.
I turn around again;
What is in will not get out.
What am I?

Answers on page 107

4. What comes with a car, goes with a car, is of no use to the car, but the car cannot go without it?

5. What travel mode has eight wheels but can only carry one passenger?

6. What has six wheels and flies?

7. I sing when I'm struck or whenever they shake me. By careful casting, the craftsmen make me.

8. What do you break just by saying its name?

9. What do you call a man who stands outside the front door all day?

24

Answers on page 108

10. Mystery Word

Each line of this puzzle is a clue to a letter.
Can you discover the hidden word?

My first is in bread but never in dear.
My second's in yell and also in cheer.
My third is in duffle and also in hood.
My fourth is in word but isn't in wood.
My fifth and my sixth are letters the same.
A baboon and a rooster have two
in their name.
My last is in temper, moody, and slam.
My whole is at home. Do you know
where I am?

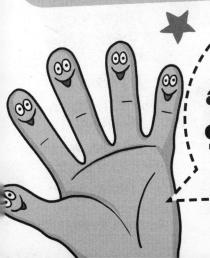

11. What advice do you get from your hands?

12. What belongs to you, but other people use it much more than you do?

13. You have to poke me in the eye to get me to do what you want. I often live in a box, but you'd never find me in a haystack. What am I?

14. Toby's mother went to the hospital to have her appendix removed. His sister went to the hospital a month later to have her tonsils taken out. A week after that, Toby needed a growth from his head removed. Why didn't he go to the hospital?

26

15. What has four legs and a back but can't walk?

16. I am buried in wood from one end to the other, but my head is on show while I hold things together. Do you know what I am?

17. I am very good at what I do. I do my job whenever you want, and I'm always on time, but nobody likes me. What am I?

Answers on page 108

27

18. What is two feet long but can be all different sizes?

19. What is being described here?
When I am full, I can point the way,
but when I am empty, I lie still.
I keep you warm on a snowy day,
but I'm useless when it's sunny.

20. What has a neck but no head, with two arms but no hands?

Answers on page 108

21. What did the shoes say to the hat before setting out on a walk?

22. I have a tongue but no mouth. I am no good to you on my own. What am I?

23. When is a coat no use to keep out the cold?

24. What five-letter word becomes shorter when you add two letters to it?

25. What has a head and a tail but no legs?

26. Rosie's mother has three daughters. She has chosen their names very carefully. The oldest is April and the middle one is May. What did she name the youngest one?

30

27. Mystery Word

Each line of this puzzle is a clue to a letter. Can you discover the hidden word?

My first is in large and also in big,
My second's in wait but isn't in twig.
My third is in car, and in ride,
and in truck.
My fourth is in sat but isn't in stuck.
My fifth is in gas but isn't in tanks.
My sixth is in creaks but isn't in cranks.
Figure out the letters, and write
each one down:
My whole can be found
by a house or in town.

28. Which burns longer, a short, fat candle or a tall, thin one?

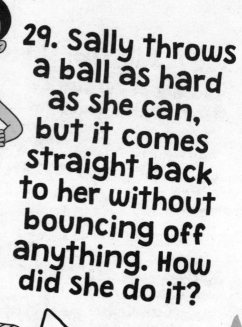

29. Sally throws a ball as hard as she can, but it comes straight back to her without bouncing off anything. How did she do it?

30. What is served but never eaten?

31. There are eight of us
To move at will:
We protect our king
From any ill.
What are we?

Answers on page 109

32. What do a comb, a zipper, and a shark all have in common?

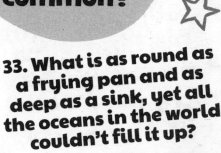

33. What is as round as a frying pan and as deep as a sink, yet all the oceans in the world couldn't fill it up?

34. There is one that has a head without an eye, and there's one that has an eye without a head. You may find the answer if you try; half of what you seek hangs upon the thread.

Answers on page 109

35. A mother has two sons who share a birthday and were born in the same year, but they are not twins. How could this happen?

36. How can you tell that birthdays are good for you?

37. What has a face and two hands but no arms or legs?

34

38. Dita has bought presents for her two sisters. Both presents do the same thing. One has many moving parts, but the other has none. One works all the time, but the other doesn't work at night. What did she buy?

39. What word begins and ends with an "e" but has only one letter in it?

40. What stays in the corner but travels around the world?

41. Which month has 28 days?

Answers on pages 109–110

42. If you screw a light bulb into a socket by turning the bulb clockwise with your right hand, which way would you turn the socket with your left hand in order to unscrew it, while holding the bulb still?

43. What has rivers but no water, cities but no people, and forests but no trees?

44. What is always hot, even if you keep it in the refrigerator?

Answers on page 110

Down on the Farm

1. What gets bigger the more you take away from it?

2. In the warm months, I wear green, both during the day and at night. As it cools, I wear yellow, but during winter, I wear white. What am I?

3. The grand old nag gallops with great delight, then it grazes on grass and sleeps at night. He's a strong friend for the farmer and me; now, how many times did you count "g"?

38

4. Where does the biggest herd of pigs live?

5. Mystery Word

Each line of this puzzle is a clue to a letter. Can you discover the hidden word?

My first is in chew and also in cud.
My second's in goad but isn't in good.
My third and my fourth are letters the same,
found in cart and in tractor, in stock
and in train.
My fifth is in lamb and in billy but not beef.
My last is in sleep and rest and relief.
My whole can be found on a farm, big or small.
Even when you can't see me, you'll
still know my call.

Answers on page 111

6. True or false? There are only two "F"s in "Farmer Fuffle."

7. A chestnut tree has an average of 6 branches, with 12 twigs on each branch and 24 nuts on each twig. How many acorns are there on one tree?

8. What is all ears and says "shhhh" but doesn't listen to a word you say?

Answers on page 112

9. Which is correct: The yolk of the egg is white, or the yolk of the eggs are white?

10. Farmer Bob was selling some eggs. His first customer said, "I'll buy half your eggs and half an egg more." His second customer said the same thing. His third customer just wanted one egg. Farmer Bob filled their orders without breaking a single egg. How many eggs did Farmer Bob have?

11. When is the best time to buy chicks?

Answers on page 112

12. What has eight legs and flies?

13. I'm white and round, but I'm not always around. When the day is at its brightest, I cannot be found. What am I?

14. Farmer Sally builds three haystacks in her north field and two in her south field. Every week afterward, for five weeks, she doubles the number in the north field and adds two more in the south field. How many haystacks will she have at the end of the harvest if she puts them all together?

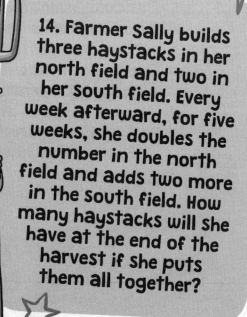

42

Answers on page 112

15. Farmer Jennings was in town for the day. He went down Main Street without stopping at the red lights and turned into a street that said "NO ENTRY." A police officer waved as he went past and didn't give him a ticket or even tell him off. Why was that?

16. When is a black dog not a black dog?

17. What do you call an experienced vet?

Answers on page 112

18. What's written here?
BOLT
TH

19. Flowers grow up in the warmth of summer. This grows down in the cold of winter. What is it?

20. You can feel it, but you can't touch it. You can hear it, but you can't see it. What is it?

Answers on page 113

21. What flies when it is born, lies around during its lifetime, and runs when it is dead?

22. Red, purple, orange, yellow, blue, and green. No one can touch me, not even a queen. What am I?

23. Daisy wakes up one morning. Without getting up or opening her eyes, she knows that it has been snowing. How is this possible?

Answers on page 113

24. What do you find in hurricanes, on a potato, and on the farmer that grows the second and sees the first coming?

25. A farmer was hard at work building a fence, when a tiny thing stopped her. Although she didn't want it, she kept on looking for it. Eventually, she took it home with her because she couldn't find it. What was it?

26. What does a dog do that a person steps into?

46

Answers on page 113

27. Mystery Word

Each line of this puzzle is a clue to a letter. Can you discover the hidden word?

My first is in goats and also in sheep.
My second's in paw but isn't in weep.
My third is in wood but isn't in grow.
My fourth's just the same as my third, don't you know.
My fifth is in bleated and cluck and in squealed.
My sixth is in stable and meadow and field.
My whole is an item you need for a horse, though the horse is quite happy without one, of course!

28. Read this riddle to a friend out loud:
"There are 20 sick sheep in a field, and six of them have to be taken to the vet. How many are left?"

Answers on page 113

29. A bridge is 3 miles long and strong enough to hold exactly 22,000 pounds but no more. A loaded truck that weighs exactly 21,999 pounds drives onto the bridge. In the middle, a sparrow that weighs 5 ounces lands on the truck, yet the bridge doesn't collapse. How could this be?

30. Most animals grow up. Which animals grow down?

31. How did the farmer find his lost daughter?

32. Forward, I am heavy, but backward, I am not. What am I?

33. How would you describe a man who does not have all his fingers on his left hand?

34. Every dawn begins with me.
At dusk, I'm the first thing you see.
Daybreak couldn't start without what midday's middle is all about.
All through the night, I won't be found, yet in the dark, I'm still around. What am I?

35. Farmer Jones gets home after a long day harvesting. It is dark, and he is cold and hungry. He has a candle, a stove, and a fireplace, but he only has a single match. Which should he light first?

36. I fly through the air with the greatest of ease. And I am also something you do to your peas.

37. The farmer was worried that her prize currant bush would never grow back after a cold winter. What did she say when she saw it was healthy and green?

50

Answers on page 114

38. How many bricks does it take to complete a brick barn that is 30 feet by 30 feet by 40 feet and made completely of bricks?

39. I have six legs, four eyes, and five ears. What am I?

40. What always runs but never walks, often murmurs but never talks, has a bed but never sleeps, has a mouth but never eats?

41. Farmer Jake was on one side of the river, and his trusty dog, Elmer, was on the other side. There was no bridge or boat. The farmer whistled to Elmer and shouted, "Here boy! Come on!" Elmer crossed the river, and they both walked back to the farmhouse. However, Elmer didn't get wet. How can that be?

42. What always sleeps with its shoes on?

52

Answers on page 114

Mealtime Mysteries

1. Is it possible to drop an unboiled egg onto a concrete kitchen floor without cracking it?

2. What two things can you eat but never have for lunch?

3. I am a food with three letters in my name. Lose the last two, and I still sound the same.

Answers on page 115

4. Which fast food gets hotter when it sounds colder?

5. Here's a rhyme to test your head.
We'll call it "The Tale of Ruby Red."
A stick in her top,
A pit in her middle,
I'll give you a prize
If you answer this riddle.

6. How many peas are there in a pod?

Answers on page 115

7. I have some cheese.
He has some cheese, too,
and so does she.
They are all the same type of
cheese. What type is that?

8. Let us find the hidden vegetable,
Speak aloud to figure it out.
When we've found the
hidden vegetable,
Let us give a happy shout.

9. What type of cheese is made backward?

Answers on page 115

10. Mystery Word

Each line of this puzzle is a clue to a letter. Can you discover the hidden word?

My first is in pasta and soup and in pit.
My second's in biscuit, in whisk, and in whip.
My third is in ice cream, chocolate chip, and cake.
My fourth is in cooking and also in bake.
My fifth is in apple but isn't in pear.
My last is in fare but isn't in flair.
Put all the letters together to spell something that goes with cheese really well.

11. Why do snails never go to hamburger joints?

12. What begins with T, ends with T, and has T in the middle?

13. What cup can't you drink from?

14. Cows drink it, and most people have some in their coffee. What am I thinking of?

15. What has a neck and a bottom but no head?

58

Answers on page 116

16. What will you find in the middle of a pie that isn't used in a cake, turnover, or tart?

17. A braggart likes to boast, and a boat sails off from the coast. But what do you put in a toaster?

18. What kind of nut has a hole?

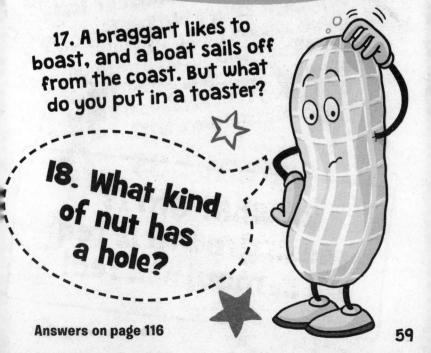

Answers on page 116

19. What letter tastes like chocolate?

20. Katie's mother went shopping for Katie's birthday party. She bought six pizzas, three cucumbers, twelve carrots, six cartons of strawberries, and forty cupcakes. Katie's brother and his friends raided the refrigerator and ate all but two cucumbers, eight carrots, a carton of strawberries, and seven cupcakes. How many carrots were left?

21. What am I?
Tree ... growth ... red.
Me ... mouth ... fed!

Answers on page 116

22. This three-letter word means "chew and swallow." Add another letter, and you can use me to cook. Add one more letter, and you can make cereal from me.

23. **What has to be broken before it is useful?**

24. I wear a crown, but I'm not a king. I have scales, but I'm not a snake. On the outside, I'm tough, but on the inside, I'm sweet. What am I?

25. I'm as round as a ball; you can eat my all. I'm delicious with butter and make a nursery for butterflies. What am I?

26. What food is written here?
POTOOOOOOOO

27.
I have the same number of oranges as my friend. How many would I have to give her, so that she has 10 more oranges than I have?

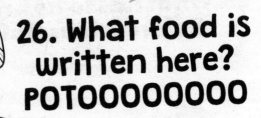

28. Mystery Word

Each line of this puzzle is a clue to a letter. Can you discover the hidden word?

My first is in tasty and also in squish.
My second's in ship but isn't in fish.
My third is in pudding and also in rice.
My fourth is in nasty but also in nice.
My fifth is the first of the vowels, it's true.
My sixth is in crunch and in lick and in chew.
My last is in dish but isn't in side, I am really healthy ... you'll eat me with pride!

29. What food has six letters, but if you chop off half of it, you are left only with the item to cook it in?

30. If your mother carries three bags of groceries into the house, and she makes you carry six bags, who has the heaviest load?

31. Go on red, and stop on green. Your teeth will know just what I mean. What am I?

32. What food starts off hard but gets softer and goes bang as it changes?

Answers on page 117

33. Which of these is the odd one out? Banana, orange, egg, pistachio, apple, avocado.

34. I wear a cap but have no head;
Pick the wrong one, and you might be dead.
I stand up straight but have no feet;
Pick the right one, and I'm good to eat.

35. Time for some arithmetic! If it takes four minutes to boil an egg, how long will it take to boil 12 eggs?

Answers on page 117

36. Two fathers and two sons are at the supermarket. They want a pizza each, and the store has plenty, but they only buy three. Why is that?

37. I have eyes but cannot see. My jacket is brown, but I don't wear clothes. My skin can be red, white, or brown, but I never need sunscreen. What am I?

Answers on page 118

38. What food sounds like a frightened person?

39. A man in a cafe orders a lunch of soup, apple pie, and black coffee. How does the waitress know he's a policeman?

40. You throw away the outside and cook the inside. Then you eat the outside and throw away the inside. What is it?

41. What is black when you buy it, red when you're making dinner, and silvery when you throw it away?

42. If an ice cream sundae with sauce costs $2.10, and the sundae costs $2 more than the sauce, how much does a sundae without sauce cost?

43. How many times does the letter "f" appear in this sentence? "Friends will not feel full of food after eating, if they feel that your food is merely a trifle!"

Answers on page 118

Riddles at School

1. Charlie's mother has just gone into his bedroom to wake him for school. She asked him a question, and she knows that he lied when he answered. How can she be so sure?

2. A teacher asks: "How may seconds are there in a year?" Amresh says, "Twelve." The teacher thinks for a moment, then says, "Yes, that's correct." How can that be?

3. What does this say?
YYUR
YYUB
ICUR
YY4 me!

4. The school librarian sets her class a challenge. "Let's say there is a banknote hidden in this library. If any of you can find it, then you may keep it as a prize. The money is slotted between pages 57 and 58 of a nonfiction title." Half of the class jump up and start pulling books off the shelves. The other half don't even leave their chairs. Why not?

5. Brutus the dog was born in 5 BC and died exactly ten years later. In what year did he die?

6. Which word has the most letters in it?

Answers on page 120

7. Some kids are playing hide-and-seek. One of them is the seeker. What is the smallest number of children hiding if: a girl is hiding to the left of a boy; a boy is hiding to the left of a boy; two boys are hiding to the right of a girl.

8. How many times does the letter "o" appear in the following sentence? "Boys often play football at school, and girls often choose to play hockey."

9. What am I thinking of? I can take away the whole and still have some left.

72

Answers on page 120

10. Mystery Word

Each line of this puzzle is a clue to a different letter. Can you discover the hidden word?

My first begins speech but also ends books.
My second is in sees but never in looks.
My third is in nice and also in not.
My fourth is a drink you can make in a pot.
My fifth is the same as my second ... that's handy!
My sixth's in vanilla and bonbon and candy.
My seventh appears in country, scene, and place.
My eighth's at the end of the tale and the race.
My whole can be written or spoken by any,
but my beginning and end are forgotten by many.
What am I?

11. What do pixies learn first at school?

Answers on page 120

12. A triangle has three sides, and a square has four. Why might you say that a bubble has two?

13. If you multiply two by itself twenty times, what answer will you get?

14. Mrs. David asked Alex to multiply five numbers together. She read out each, one at a time, but after just one number, he knew the answer. How could that be?

5x6x?=

74

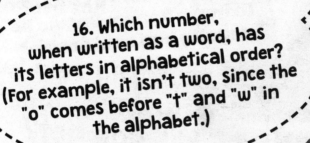

15. Can you find a way to make 1,000 with eight "8"s and four plus signs?

16. Which number, when written as a word, has its letters in alphabetical order? (For example, it isn't two, since the "o" comes before "t" and "w" in the alphabet.)

17. I'm a kind of learning you just don't get at school. Teachers love me, but pupils think I'm cruel. Your parents might help if they are cool! What am I?

Answers on page 121

18. How many ancient philosophers were born in Greece?

19. Why couldn't a centurion living in Roman Britain be legally buried in France?

20. A history teacher shows the class two coins. One is a silver coin with the date 368 BC, and the other is a bronze coin dated AD 798. Which one is worth the most?

Answers on page 121

21. What kind of ship would it take to forge an alliance between enemy pirates?

22. What flies through the air using borrowed feathers?

23. Halo of water, Tongue of wood. Skin of stone, For ages, I've stood. What am I?

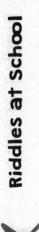

24. Recipe:
Take one season.
Add seasoning.
Roll it over and over.
What do you get?

25. I make my mark on book or card, but I will break if you press too hard.

26. What has hands but no fingers, a face but no eyes, and moves all the time without leaving the spot?

Answers on page 122

27. Two's company, and three's a crowd, so what do four and five make?

28. Mystery Word

Each line of this puzzle is a clue to a different letter. Can you discover the hidden word?

My first is in add but not in subtract.
My second is in picked but isn't in packed.
My third is in over and vacuum and five.
My fourth is in child and bright and alive.
My fifth is in good but is also in bad.
My last is in made but isn't in mad.
My whole is about learning to share things out.
Just ask your teacher what I'm all about.

Answers on page 122

29. Maisie was learning about adjectives. She asked her English teacher for help. "Miss Stuart, which is correct: My brother chose the bigger half of the cake or my brother chose the biggest half of the cake?" What did Miss Stuart say?

30. The average English word is five letters long, although it's easy to think of words with more than 10 letters. What is the longest word in the English language?

Answers on page 122

31. What Is Missing?

How quickly can you find out what is so unusual about this paragraph? It looks so ordinary that you would think that nothing is wrong with it at all, and in fact, nothing is. But it is unusual. Why? If you study it and think about it, you may find out, but I am not going to assist you in any way. You must do it without coaching. No doubt, if you work at it for long, it will dawn on you. Who knows? Go to work, and test your skill!

32. The singular forms of the verb "to be" are: "I am," "you are," and "he, she, or it is." However, can you think of an example where you would be correct in saying, "I is"?

33. Mount Everest was measured in 1856 but wasn't climbed until 1953. What was the world's highest mountain before then?

34. What is the capital of Antarctica?

35. What has four eyes and a mouth, and runs but has no legs?

36. Where is the best place in the USA to learn your multiplication tables?

37. I touch the Earth, I touch the Sky, but if I touch you, you'll surely die.

38. My feet stay warm, but my head is cold. No one can move me, I'm just too old.

39. I rest near the shore, never touching the sea. I bring worlds together, yet people cross me.

40. From my mouth belch black clouds and red–hot rain. You could sail upon my river, but your ship would be in flame.

Answers on page 123

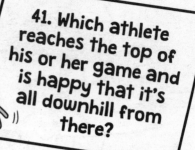

41. Which athlete reaches the top of his or her game and is happy that it's all downhill from there?

42. What sport uses a hard, white ball and begins with a "T"?.

43. Mr. Jennings the PE teacher is one of the 36% of teachers in his school who are left-handed. However, he plays racket sports right-handed. Which hand does he use to stir his coffee?

84

Answers on page 123

Underwater Riddles

1. If a fisherman brings home 20 buckets of fish, and his father brings home 40 buckets, who has the most fish?

2. What never gets any wetter, no matter how hard it rains?

3. What happens when you throw a white shell into the Red Sea?

Answers on page 124

4. What am I?
If you can hear where I come from, I am no longer there ...

5. What did the mermaid say to the salmon after his girlfriend left him for a shark?

6. This is found on land and at sea, although it can't be seen from either. It can be harnessed but not held, and it has no mouth, but it can be heard.
What is it?

Answers on page 124

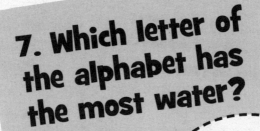

7. Which letter of the alphabet has the most water?

8. What kind of house weighs the least?

9. Four men were on a fishing trip. A storm blew up and capsized their boat, throwing all of them into the ocean. When they were rescued, every single man was still dry. Why is that?

10. Mystery Word

Each line of this puzzle is a clue to a letter. Can you discover the hidden word?

My first is in ran but isn't in far.
My second's in sea but isn't in star.
My third is in scallop and porpoise
and pearl.
My fourth's in typhoon, in twist,
and in twirl.
My fifth's in kahuna and also outside.
My first now comes back again,
like the tide.
My last is in water and ocean and home.
My whole is a god from mythical Rome.

11. How is the letter "t" like an island?

Answers on page 125

12. What phrase is written here?
CCCCCCC

13. What's the difference between an iceberg and a clothes brush?

14. A man keeps a speedboat moored in the marina. The boat's ladder hangs over the side, and at low tide, the bottom rung just touches the water. The rungs are 6 inches apart. How many rungs will be underwater when the tide rises by 2 feet?

90

Answers on page 125

15. A ship's crew is caught in a tropical storm. They all take shelter, apart from Captain Crick. He braves the elements and the lashing rain. He has no raincoat, no hat, and no umbrella. His clothes are totally soaked, rain drips from the end of his nose, and yet not a hair on his head gets wet. How can this be?

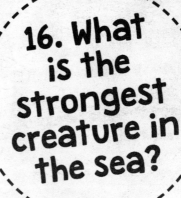

16. What is the strongest creature in the sea?

17. Imagine you are deep-sea diving. You come face to face with a great white shark. You're terrified! What should you do?

18. What sea creature can swim as fast as it likes, but it never gets away from home?

19. What kind of fish has lots of fans?

Answers on page 125

20. I have two eyes but not a tail. I swim around but am not a whale. My legs are long, but I can't walk. My head is large, but I can't talk. What am I?

21. Why are sea creatures with shells not fun to be with?

22. What runs into the ocean but stays in its bed the whole time?

23. Two dolphins are playing in the ocean. Dolphin A is behind dolphin B, but dolphin B is behind dolphin A. How can that be?

24. I am strong enough to walk on and heavy enough to crush roofs. But just a little sunlight will make me vanish! What am I?

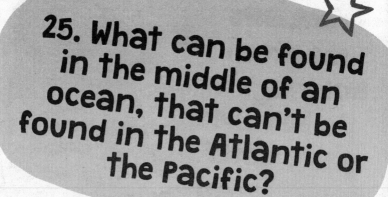

25. What can be found in the middle of an ocean, that can't be found in the Atlantic or the Pacific?

Answers on page 126

26. Mystery Word

Each line of this puzzle is a clue to a letter. Can you discover the hidden word?

My first is in cottonwood, in cedar, and in beech.
My second's in banana and also in peach.
My third is in launch and rowing and motion.
My fourth is in swordfish as well as in ocean.
My fifth is in source and also in end.
My whole is a boat you can use with a friend.

27. What has five eyes and runs through the USA?

28. What happened to the pianist who worked on a cruise ship?

29. Two cruise ships are crossing the Atlantic Ocean. The blue ship leaves Great Britain on Tuesday. The red ship leaves the United States on Thursday but is moving twice as fast. Which ship will be closer to the United States when they pass each other?

96

Answers on page 126

30. A zoologist is walking through a jungle and finds something in her pocket. It has a tail and a head but no legs. How does she know it's not dangerous?

31. An explorer is paddling up a river, when he comes to a place where it splits two ways. One way leads to a city of gold, and the other way leads to a waterfall! He has two guides with him. One guide can only tell the truth, and the other always lies. But he doesn't know which is which. What question should the explorer ask to make sure he takes the right route?

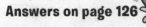

97

32. A man goes scuba diving and comes face to face with a tiger. Last year while diving, he met a bull. How can this be?

33. Dave doesn't dare go deep-sea diving in Dominica every year. Can you spell all that without the letter "d"?

34. What is the number one use of shark skin in the world?

98

Answers on page 127

35. Two pirates are standing on opposite sides of a ship. One looks west and the other east, yet they can see each other clearly. How is that?

36. What comes down but never goes up?

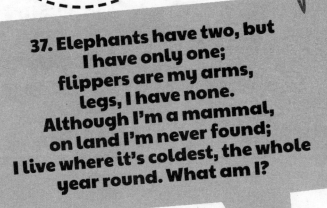

37. Elephants have two, but I have only one; flippers are my arms, legs, I have none. Although I'm a mammal, on land I'm never found; I live where it's coldest, the whole year round. What am I?

Answers on page 127

38. Can you find the name of a sea creature hidden within each of these sentences? The first one has been done for you:

A. She wanted to wear her new tuTU, NAturally.

B. Is that tiara yours, or did you borrow it?

C. In case of fire, don't panic or alarm the horses.

D. He built a lavish ark in the yard for them to play on.

39. I'm the part of the bird that's not in the sky. I can surf over the ocean but always stay dry. What am I?

100

Answers on page 127

Answers

Animal Riddles

Pages 6-7

1. Swap the "P" in polar bear, and it becomes "solar bear."
2. A sheep.
3. A snail. (You couldn't carry your home!)
4. The bear has gone in a straight line 3 miles north to the North Pole, then 2 miles onward, now heading south.
5. They don't ... they have bear feet!
6. Because if they lived by the bay, they'd be bagels!

Pages 8-9

7. Baby giraffes.
8. A mole.
9. A snake.
10. Footsteps.
11. Because they taste funny!

Pages 10-11

12. It's a computer lesson,
    and they are computer mice.
13. A carpet!
14. Your appointment is at tooth-hurty!
15. Because they are always spotted.
16. Warthog.

Pages 12-13

17. He gets closer and closer,
    but he never reaches the edge.
18. A fox.
19. Out of bounds!
20. The riddle says it is not to one side of
    him. That's because it is on the other
    side of him!
21. A lonfsh.
22. An egg.

Pages 14-15

23. His horse is named Friday.

24. Lioness. Take away "l," "i," "s," and "s," and "one" is left. The lion is "king of the beasts," so she must be queen!

25. "Bye, son!" (Bison ... get it?)

26. First, he takes the rat across and rows back. Then he takes the snake across, but when he rows back, he brings the rat with him. He leaves the rat again and rows over with the grain. He rows back with an empty boat, then finally takes the rat across.

Pages 16-17

27. You don't; you get down (feathers) from a duck.

28. Lots of animals can. Elephants can't jump!

29. A dog. In the winter, it wears a coat, but in the summer, it wears a coat and pants!

30. The other end of the string isn't tied to anything.

31. Humans. They crawl in early life, walk on two legs as adults, and by the end of their life, they use a walking stick to help them.

32. When it is a chess piece.

Pages 18-19

33. When it is a cob (a male swan).
34. A person riding a horse.
35. A hippo.
36. None. Peacocks are male and don't lay eggs.
37. Fur or hair.
38. The letter "g."

Page 20

39. Just one ... me! When I met them, they were coming from the opposite direction, away from St. Ives.
40. A zebra.

Around the Home

Pages 22-23

1. Glass!
2. The carpet.
3. A key.
4. The noise of the car's engine.
5. Roller skates.
6. A garbage truck (it is surrounded by flies, the insects, because of the garbage).

Pages 24-25

7. A bell.
8. Silence.
9. Matt!
10. Bedroom.
11. Fingertips!

Pages 26-27

12. Your name.
13. A needle.
14. He just went to the hairdresser
    for a haircut.
15. A chair.
16. A nail.
17. An alarm clock.

Pages 28-29

18. A pair of shoes.
19. A glove.
20. A turtleneck jumper.
21. You go on a-head ... We'll follow
    you on foot!
22. A shoe.
23. When it's a coat of paint.

Pages 30-31

24. "Short."
25. A coin.
26. Rosie.
27. Garage.
28. Neither; candles burn shorter.

Pages 32-33

29. She threw the ball straight up in the air.
30. A tennis ball (and also a volleyball and a shuttlecock).
31. Pawns in a chess game.
32. Teeth.
33. A colander or sieve.
34. A pin and a needle.

Pages 34-35

35. They are two sons out of triplets (or more).
36. The more you have, the longer you'll live!
37. A clock.
38. A clock and a sundial. They both tell the time, but the sundial does not work at night.

39. Envelope.
40. A stamp.
41. All of them! And some have even more ...

Page 36

42. Clockwise. It doesn't matter which hand you use, but it does matter whether you're turning the bulb or the socket.
43. A map.
44. Hot sauce.

Down on the Farm

Pages 38-39

1. A hole.
2. A deciduous tree.
3. There are 10. Don't forget the last "g" that is part of the question!
4. In a sty-scraper!
5. Cattle.

Pages 40-41

6. True. There are only two capital "F"s. The others are lower case "f"s.

7. None. Acorns grow on oak trees, not chestnut trees.

8. A field of corn.

9. Neither. The yolk is yellow!

10. Seven. He sold four eggs to the first customer (half of seven is 3 and a half plus the other half = 4 eggs), and two to the second customer (there are three eggs remaining, and half of three is one and a half. Add the other half = 2 eggs.) His third customer had one egg. So 4+2+1 = 7.

11. When they are going cheap!

Pages 42-43

12. Two cows in a field.

13. The Moon.

14. One!

15. Farmer Jennings was walking through town.

16. When it's a greyhound.

17. A veteran.

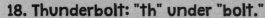

Answers

Pages 44-45
18. Thunderbolt: "th" under "bolt."
19. An icicle.
20. The wind.
21. Snow.
22. A rainbow.
23. Daisy is a cow and sleeps in a field.

Pages 46-47
24. Eyes.
25. A splinter.
26. Pants.
27. Saddle.
28. 14. It's "20 SICK sheep," but your friend will hear "26."

Pages 48-49

29. The truck would have burned off more than 5 grams of fuel by the time it reaches the middle of the bridge. Therefore, the sparrow's weight would have no effect.
30. Ducks or geese.
31. He tractor down!
32. A ton. Written backward, it spells "not"!
33. Normal. It's best to have half your fingers on each hand.
34. The letter "d."

Page 50-51

35. The match.
36. Swallow.
37. "That's a re-leaf."
38. Just one to complete it.
39. A farmer on horseback chewing an ear of corn.
40. A river.

Page 52

41. The river is frozen.
42. A horse.

Mealtime Mysteries

Page 54-55

1. Yes ... it's highly unlikely that an unboiled egg will crack a concrete floor.
2. Breakfast and dinner.
3 Pea.
4. A chili dog is hotter (spicier) than a hot dog.
5. A cherry.
6. There is one "p" in "a pod."

Page 56-57

7. Nacho cheese ("not your cheese")!
8. Lettuce. Just listen as you say it!
9. Edam (read it backward).
10. Pickle.
11. They're not into fast food.

Page 58-59

12. Teapot.
13. A hiccup.
14. Water. Cows make milk, but they don't drink it!
15. A bottle.
16. The letter "i."
17. Bread.
18. A doughnut.

Page 60-61

19. A brown "e."
20. Eight carrots.
21. An apple.
22. Eat, heat, wheat.
23. An egg.
24. A pineapple.

Page 62-63

25. Cabbage.
26. Potatoes (pot + 8 Os).
27. Five. You start with 20 oranges each. You'll end up with 15, and your friend will have 25.
28. Spinach.
29. Potato (take away "ato," and you're left with "pot").

Page 64-65

30. Your mother. You are only carrying bags, not groceries.
31. A watermelon.
32. Popcorn.
33. The apple. It is the only one that can be eaten without removing its outer layer.
34. A mushroom.
35. Four minutes. The arithmetic part was to just there confuse you.

Answers

Page 66-67

36. There are only three people: Grandfather, father, and son (the grandfather is also father to the father).
37. A potato.
38. Ice cream.
39. He is wearing his uniform.
40. Corn on the cob.
41. The charcoal in a barbecue.

Page 68

42. The sundae without sauce costs $2.05. The sauce costs 5c, which is $2 less.

43. 10.

118

Riddles at School

Page 70-71

1. She asked if he was asleep, and he said, "Yes"!

2. There are twelve "seconds" in a year: January 2nd, February 2nd, March 2nd, and so on ...

3. Read it out loud: Too wise you are, too wise you be, I see you are too wise for me!

4. They may be lazy or rude, or they may have figured out that there's no way to hide something between pages 57 and 58 of a book, since they are the two sides of the same piece of paper.
5. AD 6. There is no year 0, so when you count, you jump from 1 BC to AD 1.
6. A mailbox or postbox.

Page 72-73
7. The smallest possible number is three: girl, boy, boy.
8. 11.
9. The word "wholesome."
10. Sentence.
11. The elfabet.

Page 74-75

12. A bubble has an inside and an outside.
13. You will always get the answer "four," no matter how many times you attempt it: $2 \times 2 = 4$.
14. The first number was zero, which means it doesn't matter what other numbers are given, the answer will always be zero.
15. $888 + 88 + 8 + 8 + 8 = 1,000$
16. Forty.
17. Homework.

Page 76-77

18. None. They were babies when they were born.
19. Because he was still alive.
20. The one dated AD 798, since the other must be a fake. No one in the year 368 BC could have predicted the dating system we use (they wouldn't know how many years BC it was!).
21. Friendship.
22. An arrow.
23. A castle.

Page 78-79

24. A somersault: Summer + salt.
25. A pencil.
26. A clock.
27. Nine. 4 + 5 = 9.
28. Divide.

Page 80-81

29. Neither is right. Two halves of a cake are equal in size.
30. "Language" is the longest word in "the English language."
31. The whole text does not contain the letter "e," even though it is one of the most commonly used letters in the English language.
32. "I" is the ninth letter of the alphabet, or "I" is one of the five vowels.

Page 82-83

33. It was still Mount Everest. Measuring or climbing it didn't change its height.
34. The letter "A."
35. The Mississippi River.
36. Times Square.
37. Lightning.
38. A mountain.
39. A bridge.
40. A volcano.

Page 84

41. A skier.
42. Golf. It begins with a tee!
43. He really ought to use a spoon.

Underwater Riddles

Page 86-87

1. The fisherman ... if his father's buckets are empty.
2. The ocean.
3. It makes a splash. (Of course, it doesn't turn pink! Don't be silly ...)
4. A seashell. If you can hear the sound of the ocean by holding it to your ear, the shell is no longer in the ocean.
5. Don't worry ... there are plenty more fish in the sea.
6. The wind.

Page 88-89
7. The "c."
8. A lighthouse.
9. All four men were married, so no "single" men were there to get wet!
10. Neptune.
11. It's in the middle of water.

Page 90-91
12. The seven seas.
13. One crushes boats, and the other brushes coats!
14. None. The boat and the ladder will rise with the tide.
15. He is bald.
16. A mussel.

Page 92-93
17. Stop imagining!
18. A turtle.
19. A starfish.
20. An octopus.
21. They are so crabby!
22. A river.

Page 94-95

23. They have their backs to each other.

24. Ice.

25. The letter "e."

26. Canoe.

27. The Mississippi River.

Page 96-97

28. She got middle—C sickness.

29. When the two ships meet, they will both be exactly the same distance from the United States.

30. It's a coin.

31. He should ask one guide, "Which way would the other guide tell me to go?" ... and then take the opposite route. Here's why: The guide who tells the truth will honestly tell the explorer that the liar will tell him the wrong way. The guide who lies will tell the explorer a fib about the honest man's answer. Either way, the explorer needs to do the opposite of what he is told.

Page 98-99

32. They are both types of shark.
33. Yes ... "all that"!
34. Covering sharks, of course!
35. The pirates are facing inward, not outward.
36. Rain, hail, or snow.
37. A narwhal (which has a single tusk instead of two, like an elephant).

Page 100

38. B. RAY: Is that tiaRA Yours, or did you borrow it?
    C. CORAL: In case of fire, don't paniC OR ALarm the horses.
    D. SHARK: He built a laviSH ARK in the yard for them to play on.
39. The bird's shadow.